Usborne
Build your own
DRAGONS &
FANTASY WARRIORS
Sticker Book

Illustrated by Gong Studios

Designed by Marc Maynard and Keith Furnival
Written by Simon Tudhope

The magical land of Ravenhold is filled with powerful dragons and warriors.
Many of them are illustrated in this book. Some will help a weary adventurer,
but others can be dangerous — or even deadly. Once you've read about a
dragon or warrior, you can look at the map below to see where they live.

Drakash

High above Ravenhold, Drakash burns like a second sun. He makes his own lightning and lets it flow through his veins. Then... CRACK! His target disappears in a flash of light.

STATISTICS

- **Attack power:** 8
- **Speed:** 7
- **Size:** 7
- **Age:** 130 years old
- **Realm:** The Urghar Wildlands

Murgarna

The witch-queen of Morven Castle has turned herself into a dragon. Perched high on the clifftops, an unearthly sound rips from her throat. It reaches into the minds of the soldiers below, and drives them wild with fear. As the army scatters, she tips back her head and unleashes a victorious cry.

STATISTICS

- **Attack power:** 9
- **Speed:** 5
- **Size:** 6
- **Age:** 220 years old
- **Realm:** Morven Island

Parsek

Stonewall is under siege, and Parsek is the people's best hope. Faster than a speeding arrow he carries a messenger over the enemy soldiers. Together, they'll fly to the four corners of the kingdom and raise an army to save the city.

STATISTICS

- **Attack power:** 5
- **Speed:** 10
- **Size:** 6
- **Age:** 50 years old
- **Realm:** Stonewall

Endelung

The ocean churns as a monstrous creature bursts from the deep. It looms over the ship below, and a lightning flash reveals its face. The captain cries: "It's Endelung – pirate's doom! She'll drown us all to steal our loot!"

STATISTICS

- **Attack power:** 8
- **Speed:** 5
- **Size:** 10
- **Age:** 450 years old
- **Realm:** The Endless Sea

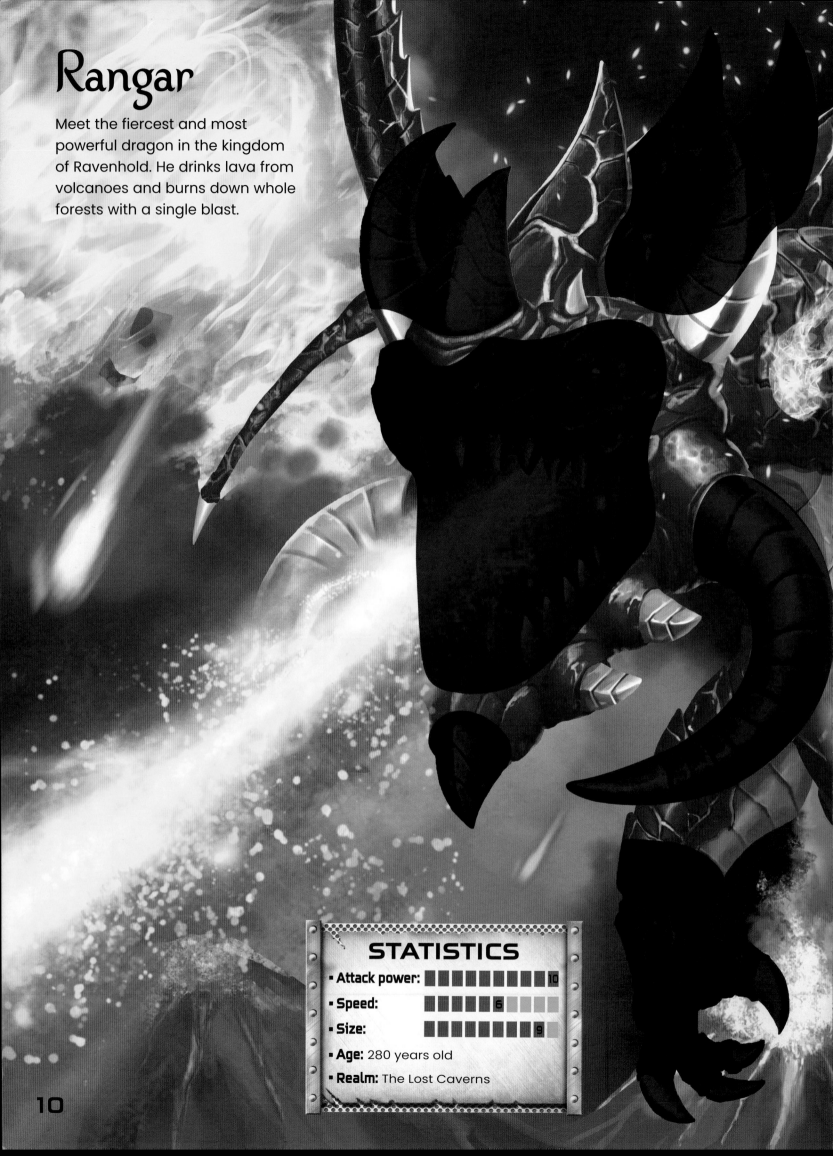

Rangar

Meet the fiercest and most powerful dragon in the kingdom of Ravenhold. He drinks lava from volcanoes and burns down whole forests with a single blast.

STATISTICS

- **Attack power:** 10
- **Speed:** 6
- **Size:** 9
- **Age:** 280 years old
- **Realm:** The Lost Caverns

Wugmeer

In the steaming heart of Gloamlands Swamp, Wugmeer lies completely still. He looks just like a rotting log. But his eyes are following something long and red, moving underwater. With a whip of his tail he brings a snake to the surface... straight to his waiting jaws!

STATISTICS

- **Attack power:** 4
- **Speed:** 7
- **Size:** 5
- **Age:** 300 years old
- **Realm:** Gloamlands Swamp

Magaloki

Most people in Ravenhold think this three-headed dragon is a myth – but they're wrong. Magaloki really does exist, and really does have three heads. The first breathes ice, the second breathes fire, and the third head turns you to stone.

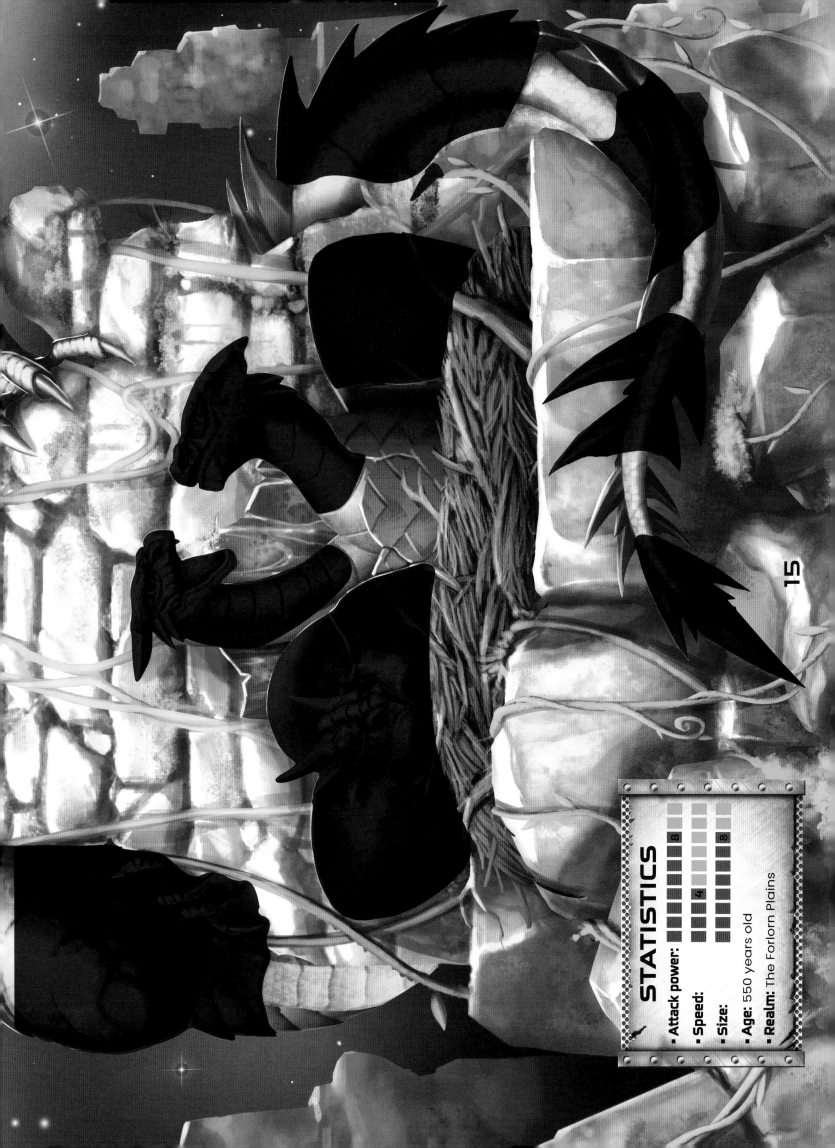

STATISTICS

- Attack power: ⬛⬛⬛⬛⬛⬛⬛⬛ 8
- Speed: ⬛⬛⬛⬛ 4
- Size: ⬛⬛⬛⬛⬛⬛⬛⬛ 8
- Age: 550 years old
- Realm: The Forlorn Plains

The Drakavi

As night approaches the Drakavi awaken. Down below, an explorer sees hundreds of little lights appear in the treetops. But then the lights start to swirl and grow... and blink. Those aren't lights – they're eyes! As the swarm descends, he starts to run.

STATISTICS

- **Attack power:** 6
- **Speed:** 8
- **Size:** 2
- **Age:** life-expectancy of 30 years
- **Realm:** Grimwold Forest

17

Bagudush

The walls of Pellanor have stood for hundreds of years, but they've never faced anything like Bagudush. With a fearsome roar and a swing of her tail, she sends an ancient watchtower crashing to earth.

STATISTICS

- Attack power: 8
- Speed: 6
- Size: 7
- Age: 180 years old
- Realm: The Luru Plains

Stalagar

At first, the cavern looks empty...
except for the treasure. But touch
a single coin or gem, and the icicles
start to creak and crack. Stalagar
rears up from the floor! He comes
to life to protect his hoard, and can
freeze you solid with a single breath.

STATISTICS

- **Attack power:** 7
- **Speed:** 2
- **Size:** 8
- **Age:** 460 years old
- **Realm:** The Frozen Sea

Slygarr

Deep underground, a sorcerer found this dragon's bones and brought it back to life. A green fire kindled in the empty skull, and a soft voice hissed: "I am Slygarr, queen of all dragons – and now I shall rule again!"

STATISTICS

- **Attack power:** 9
- **Speed:** 7
- **Size:** 7
- **Age:** 960 years old
- **Realm:** The Dark Mountains

Glossary

- **KINDLED:** started burning

- **LAVA:** incredibly hot, liquid rock that erupts from a volcano. When it cools, it turns back into rock.

- **LOOT:** stolen treasure

- **MYTH:** something that doesn't exist or didn't happen

- **REARS UP:** rises

- **SIEGE:** when soldiers surround a castle so that no one can get in or out, and the people inside starve

- **SORCERER:** a wizard

- **TAMED:** trained to live with humans

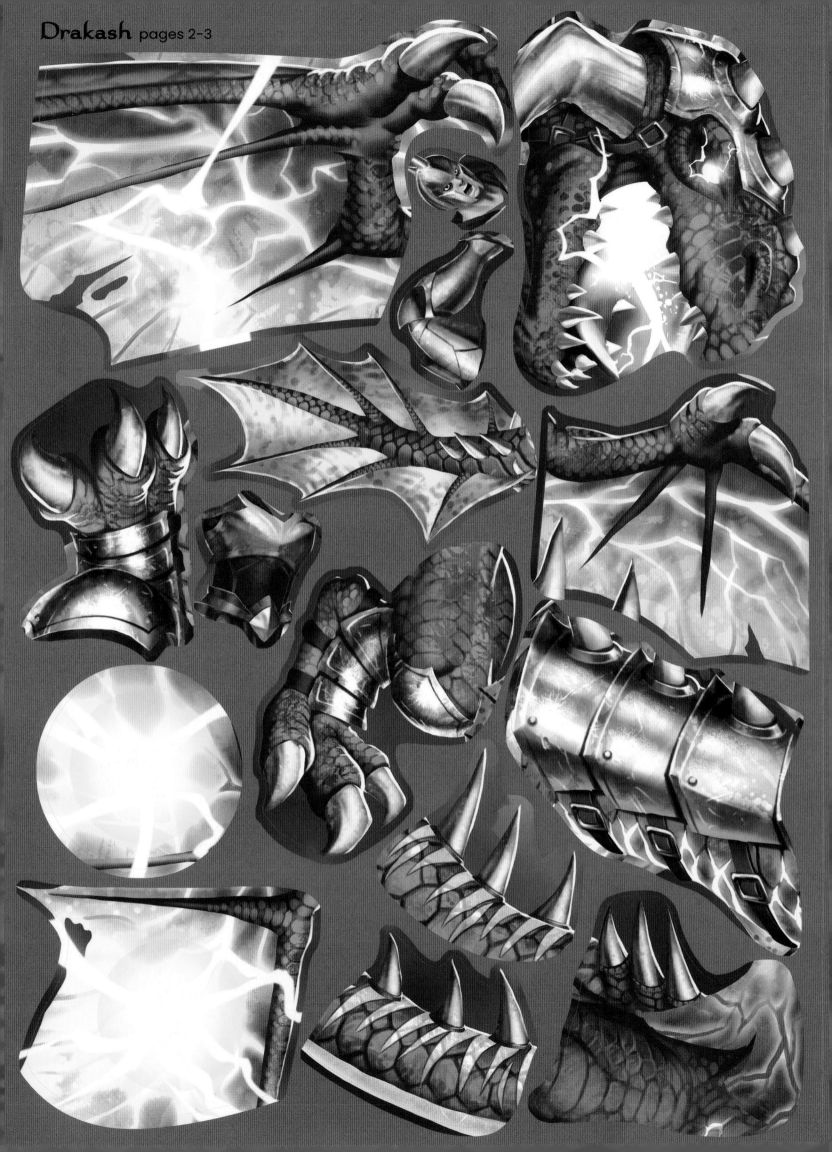

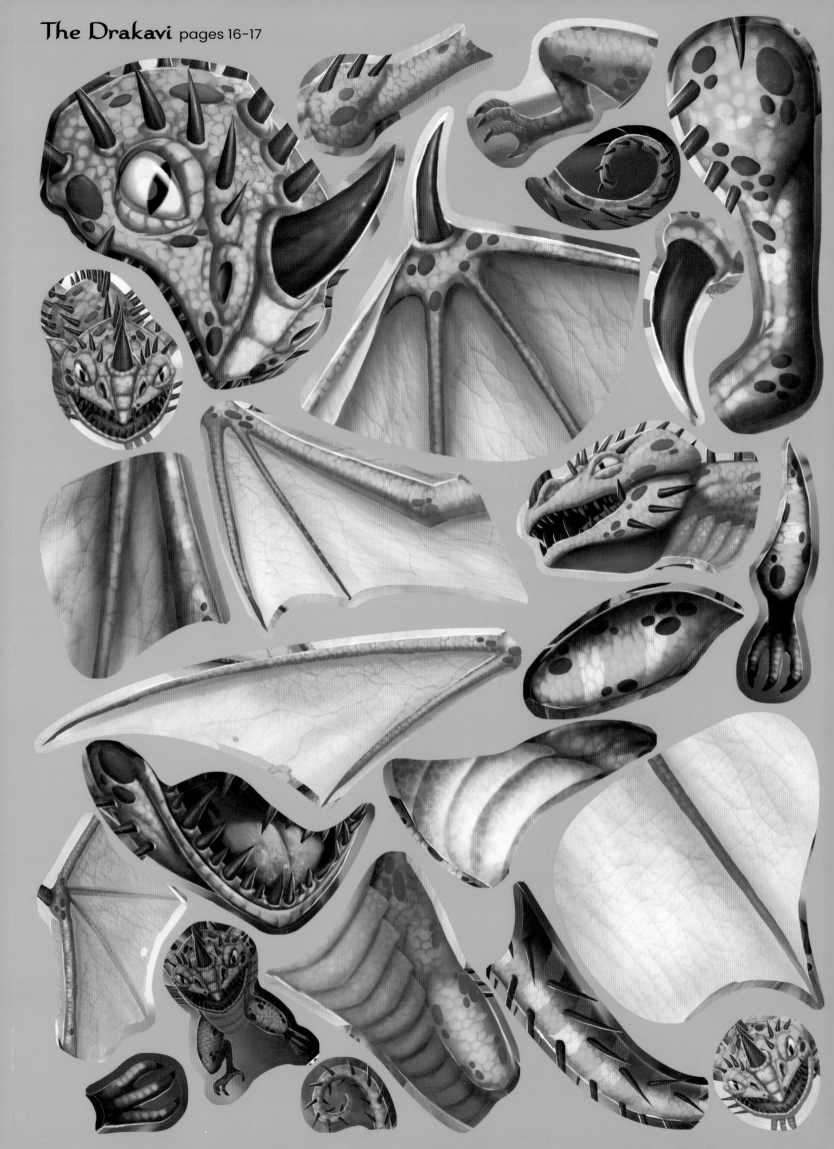

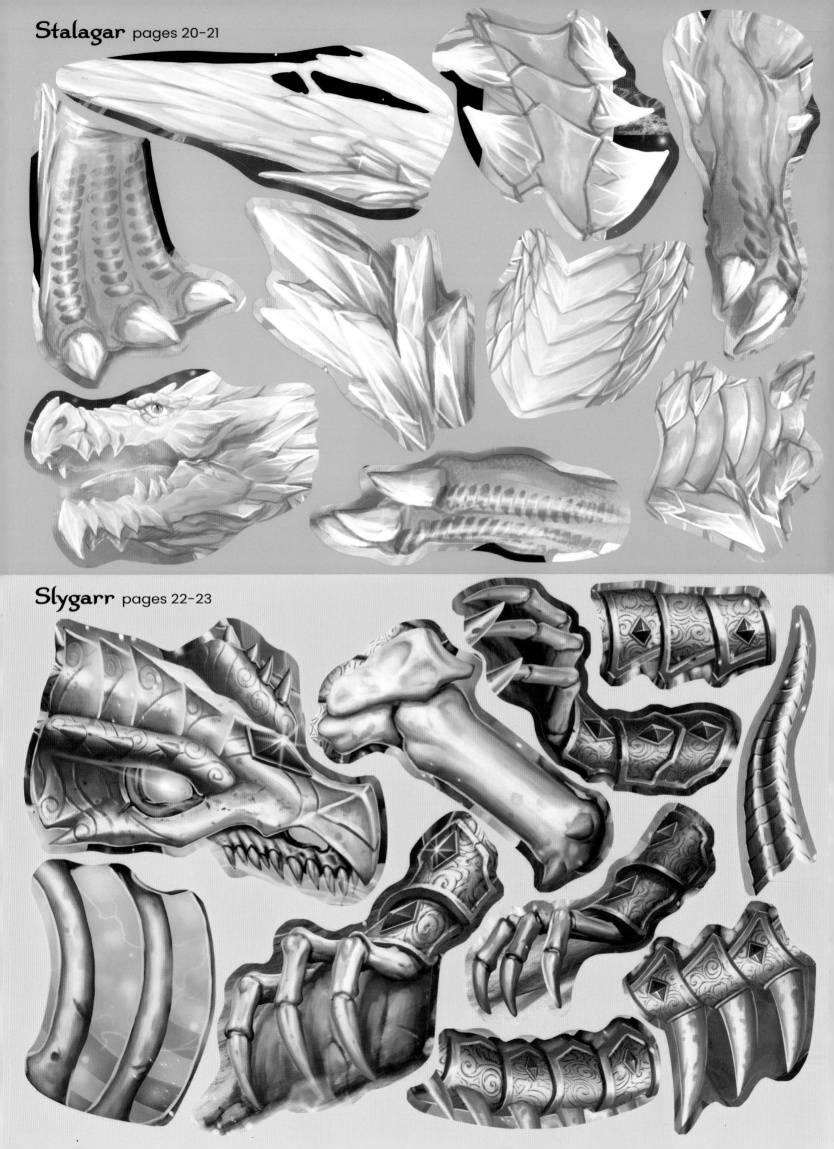

FANTASY WARRIORS

Ramona

Ramona's bow is one of the most feared weapons in the kingdom of Ravenhold. Made from the bones of an ancient dragon, it can strike her target from over a mile away.

STATISTICS

- Skill: 9
- Bravery: 8
- Intelligence: 6
- Attack power: 8
- Realm: Grimwold Forest

Nagar

They appear like a swarm of bats on the horizon, but the jets of flame give them away – the sky pirates are coming! Nagar leads the raid, his fire sword pointed at the doomed city below.

STATISTICS

- Skill: 7
- Bravery: 8
- Intelligence: 6
- Attack power: 9
- Realm: The Lost Caverns

27

Molakor

Molakor doesn't need to fight his enemies – not when he has control over time itself! In a blinding flash he turns a young warrior into an ancient pile of bones. Look closely and you'll see his ghost, trapped forever inside Molakor's staff.

STATISTICS

- **Skill:** 8
- **Bravery:** 6
- **Intelligence:** 10
- **Attack power:** 10
- **Realm:** The Urghar Wildlands

Zanak

Meet the mightiest warrior in the Khaldesh army. The enemies' shields rattle as he steps forward and roars his challenge: "WHICH OF YOU COWARDS DARES FACE ME IN COMBAT?"

STATISTICS
- **Skill:** 7
- **Bravery:** 8
- **Intelligence:** 5
- **Attack power:** 8
- **Realm:** The Khaladz Desert

Griskin

Deep inside his mountain lair, Griskin cackles as he mixes his potions. And today he's concocted a fiendish brew. Smashing it down at the feet of his foes, he turns them all into slugs!

STATISTICS

- **Skill:** 7
- **Bravery:** 3
- **Intelligence:** 8
- **Attack power:** 6
- **Realm:** The Dark Mountains

Rakael

The Dragon Stone glows bright green as Rakael summons the beast within: "Ancient spirit, scourge of Ravenhold, AWAKE and unleash your fury!"

STATISTICS

- **Skill:** 6
- **Bravery:** 7
- **Intelligence:** 7
- **Attack power:** 10
- **Realm:** The Lost Caverns

Elador

The city of Stonewall is about to fall. With all hope lost, Elador unsheathes the Sword of Souls. Ancient spells flicker across its blade and reach into the minds of his foes. They drop their weapons and clutch their heads. "Run," the sword whispers. "Run or be cursed forever!"

STATISTICS

- **Skill:** 8
- **Bravery:** 8
- **Intelligence:** 7
- **Attack power:** 10
- **Realm:** Stonewall

Ardana

Storm clouds gather as Ardana takes to the skies. Grabbing bolts of lightning and hurling them to earth, she turns mighty warriors into piles of ash.

STATISTICS

- Skill: `9`
- Bravery: `6`
- Intelligence: `6`
- Attack power: `9`
- Realm: Pellanor

Narien

Narien is queen of the Janush – a tribe of warriors who can turn into wolves. She rides into battle on her brother's back, gripping her boomerang blade.

STATISTICS

- Skill: 8
- Bravery: 9
- Intelligence: 8
- Attack power: 7
- Realm: The Frozen Sea

Karaka

You don't want to anger Karaka – as some bandits are about to discover. They dart in and out like a swarm of flies, but he's surprisingly quick for a man of his size...

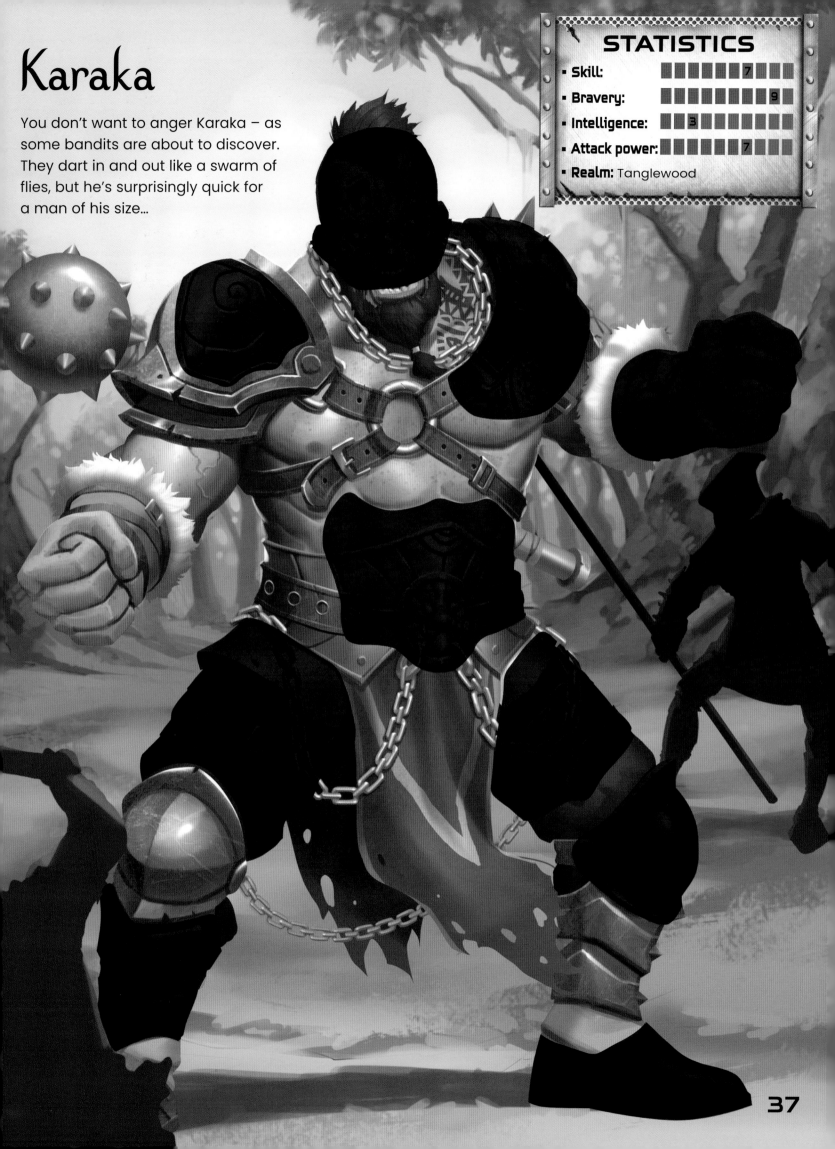

STATISTICS

- **Skill:** 7
- **Bravery:** 9
- **Intelligence:** 3
- **Attack power:** 7
- **Realm:** Tanglewood

37

Aegis

Aegis streaks across the battlefield like a shooting star. Panicked soldiers try to bring her down, but their arrows turn to ashes in mid-flight. With a victorious cry she lets her sun-spear fly... and her target falls in a flash of light.

STATISTICS

- **Skill:** 10
- **Bravery:** 9
- **Intelligence:** 8
- **Attack power:** 7
- **Realm:** The Luru Plains

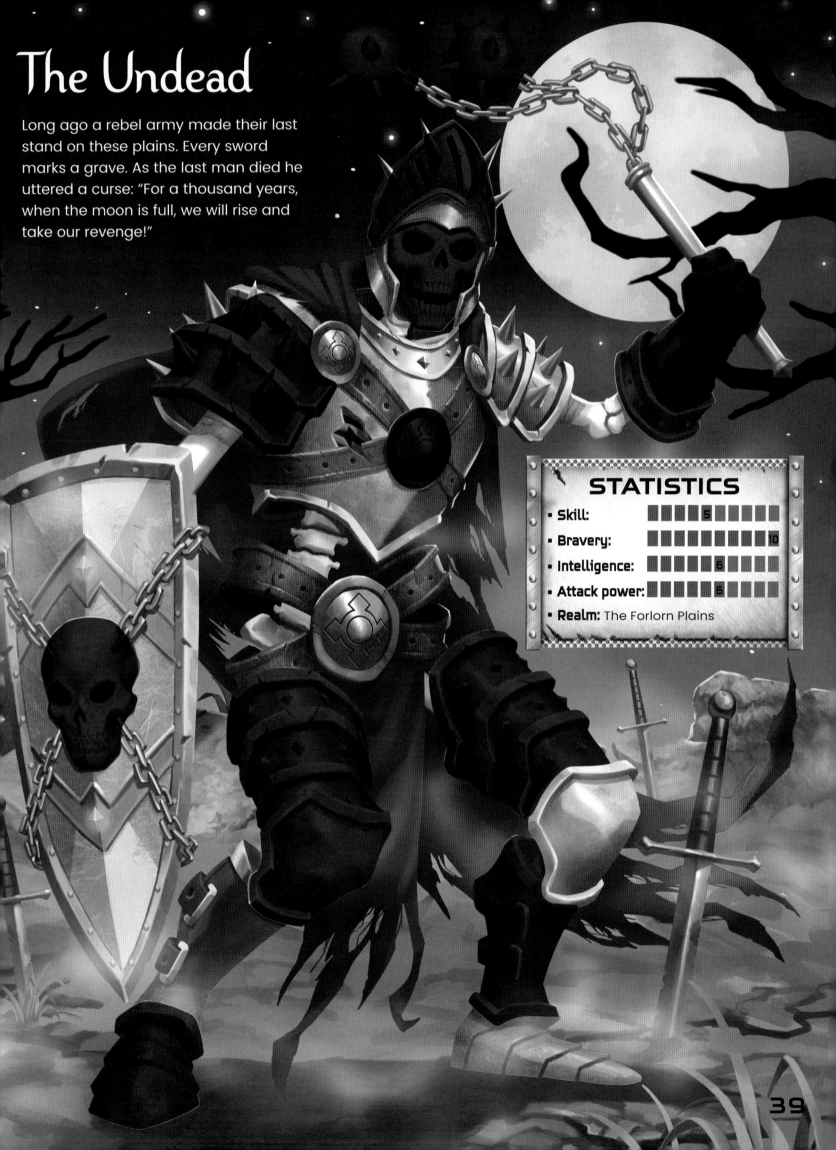

The Undead

Long ago a rebel army made their last stand on these plains. Every sword marks a grave. As the last man died he uttered a curse: "For a thousand years, when the moon is full, we will rise and take our revenge!"

STATISTICS

- **Skill:** 5
- **Bravery:** 10
- **Intelligence:** 6
- **Attack power:** 6
- **Realm:** The Forlorn Plains

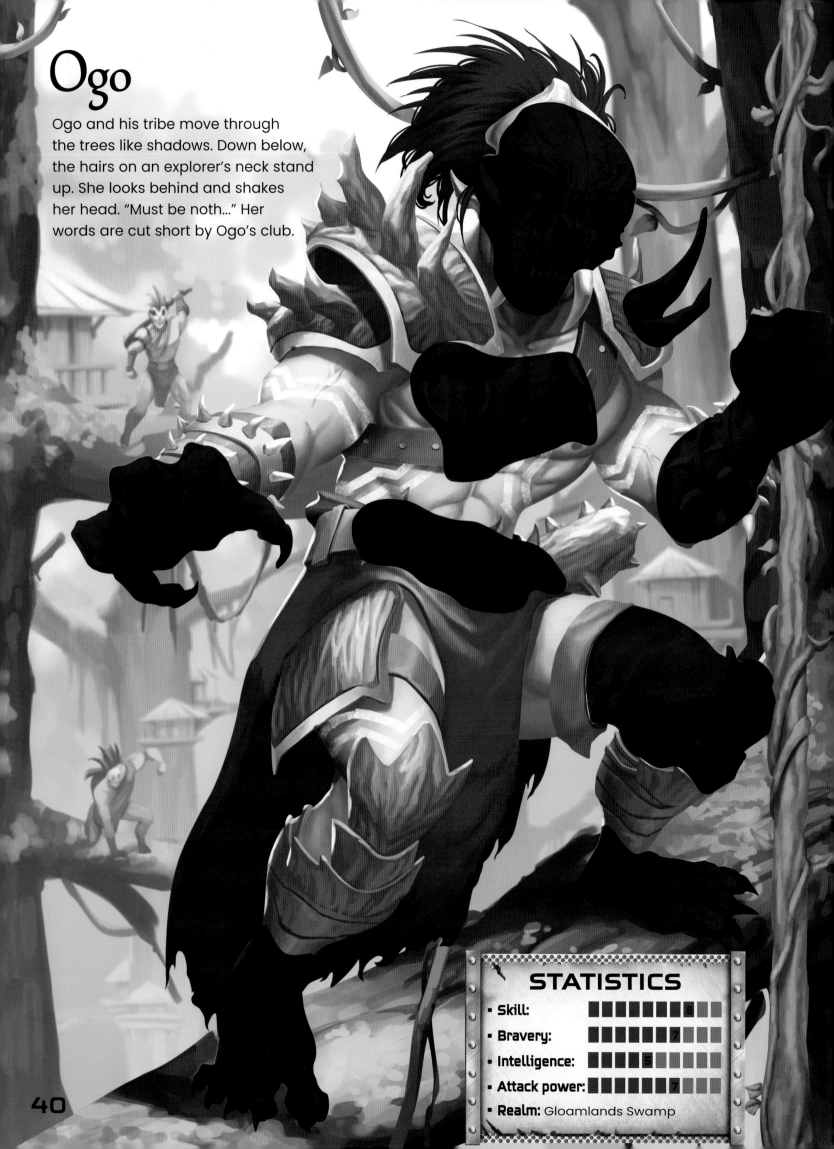

Ogo

Ogo and his tribe move through the trees like shadows. Down below, the hairs on an explorer's neck stand up. She looks behind and shakes her head. "Must be noth..." Her words are cut short by Ogo's club.

STATISTICS

- Skill: `8`
- Bravery: `7`
- Intelligence: `5`
- Attack power: `7`
- Realm: Gloamlands Swamp

Lokus

The call of his red-eyed raven echoes around the canyon, directing Lokus towards the exhausted fugitive. The chase has gone on for weeks, but now it's over. "Dead or alive?" he snarls. "The choice is yours."

STATISTICS

- Skill: 9
- Bravery: 7
- Intelligence: 8
- Attack power: 7
- Realm: The Urghar Wildlands

41

Pelaseer

The wind whistles and wails as it whips the sails of an unfortunate ship. But there's something else... A battle cry? Too late the lookout spies the faces in the waves. And then she appears on the tallest crest: the Ocean's Queen... and sailor's doom!

STATISTICS

- Skill: 8
- Bravery: 8
- Intelligence: 7
- Attack power: 10
- Realm: The Endless Sea

43

Koba

Koba the dragon-slayer waits for her moment to strike. As the beast swoops low, she raises her shield and lashes her tail around its neck. With a deafening screech it crashes to earth.

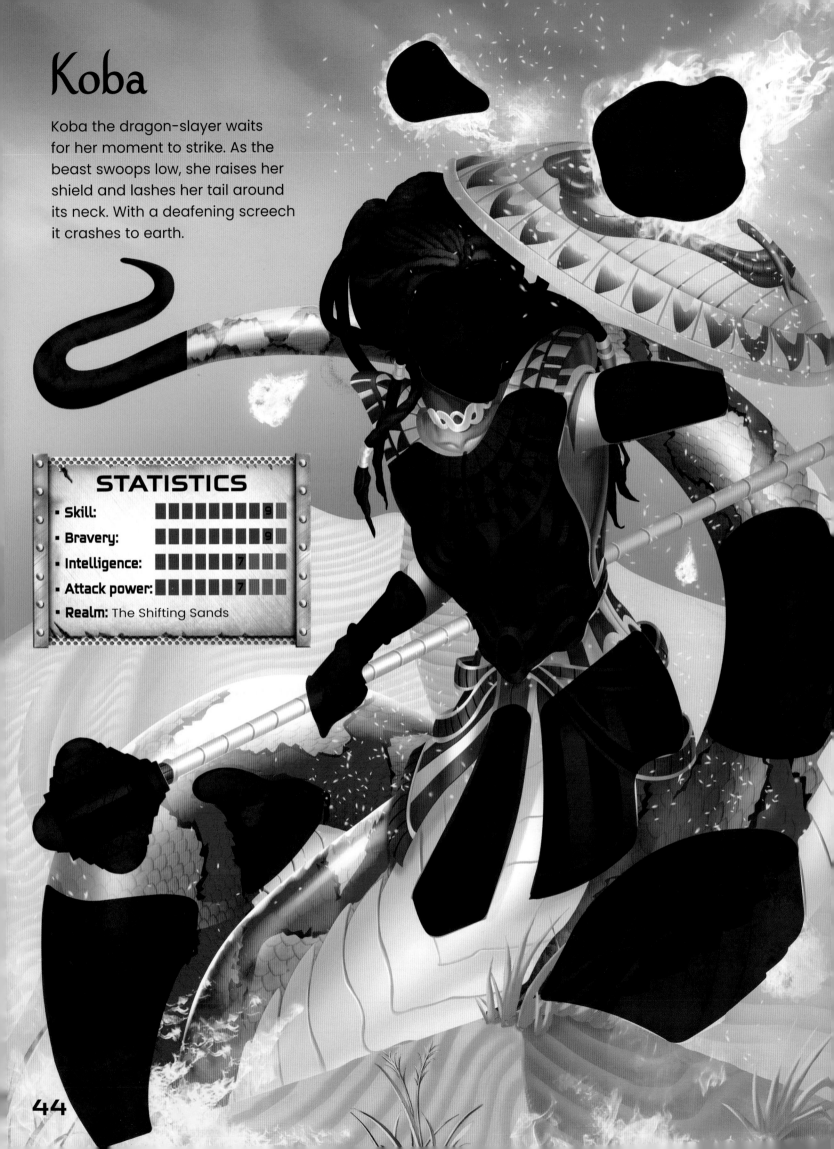

STATISTICS

- **Skill:** 9
- **Bravery:** 9
- **Intelligence:** 7
- **Attack power:** 7
- **Realm:** The Shifting Sands

Firebeard

Firebeard is the dwarves' mightiest champion – and in his hand is the Star Hammer. Forged from a metal discovered deep underground, it can turn boulders to dust with one smash.

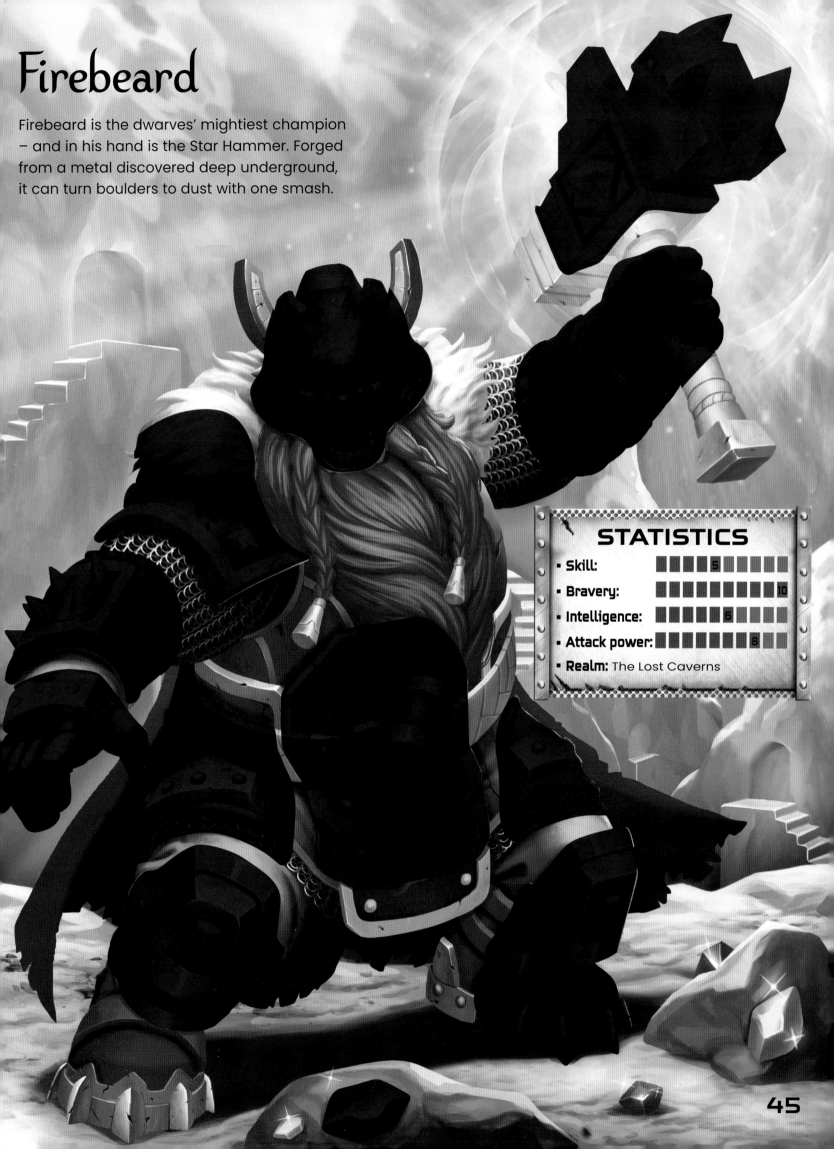

STATISTICS

- **Skill:** 5
- **Bravery:** 10
- **Intelligence:** 6
- **Attack power:** 8
- **Realm:** The Lost Caverns

Malrug

As an army approaches the city of Pellanor, Malrug stomps out to meet it. He's an alchemist who's built a mechanical suit, powered by mysterious means. "HALT!" he roars. "You have twenty seconds to surrender!"

STATISTICS

- **Skill:** 7
- **Bravery:** 7
- **Intelligence:** 9
- **Attack power:** 9
- **Realm:** Pellanor

47

Glossary

- **ALCHEMIST:** a type of scientist who does experiments and tries to transform one substance into another: for example, iron into gold

- **BOOMERANG:** a thin, curved object that can be thrown so that it spins in a wide arc and returns to the thrower

- **CONCOCT:** create

- **CREST:** the top of something. For example, the top of a wave.

- **FIENDISH:** cruel or nasty

- **FOE:** enemy

- **LOOKOUT:** a person who keeps watch for danger. On a ship they stand near the top of a mast.

- **REBEL:** someone who doesn't follow the orders of their leader

- **SCOURGE:** something that causes suffering

- **SHOOTING STAR:** a lump of rock, metal and ice that burns as it falls through a planet's atmosphere, making a streak of light in the sky

Edited by Sam Taplin

This edition first published in 2023 by Usborne Publishing Limited, 83–85 Saffron Hill, London EC1N 8RT, United Kingdom. usborne.com

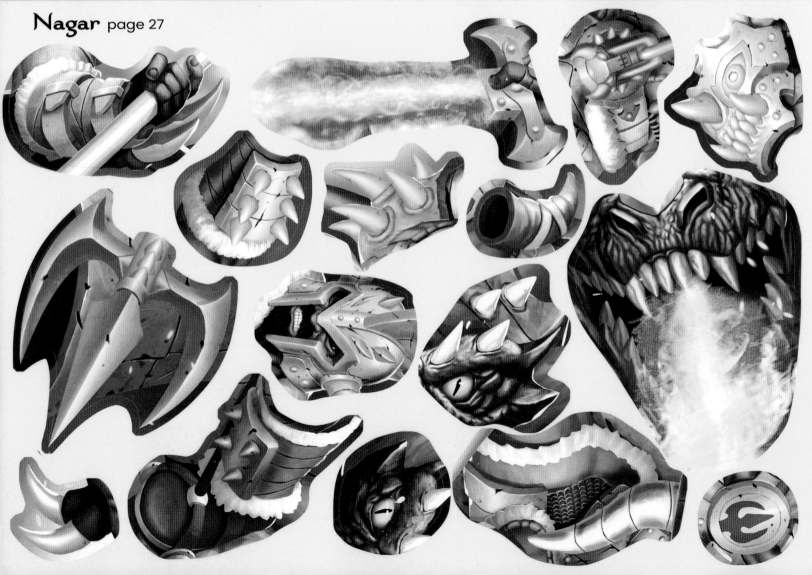

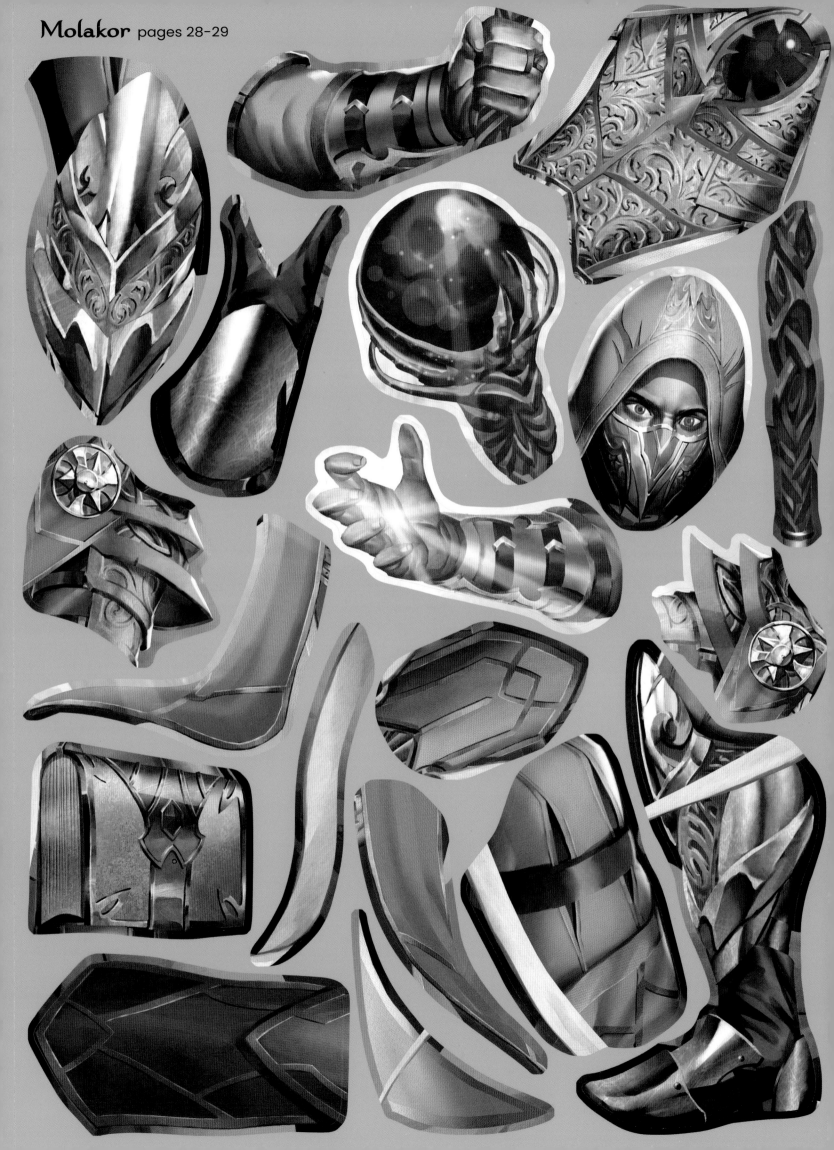

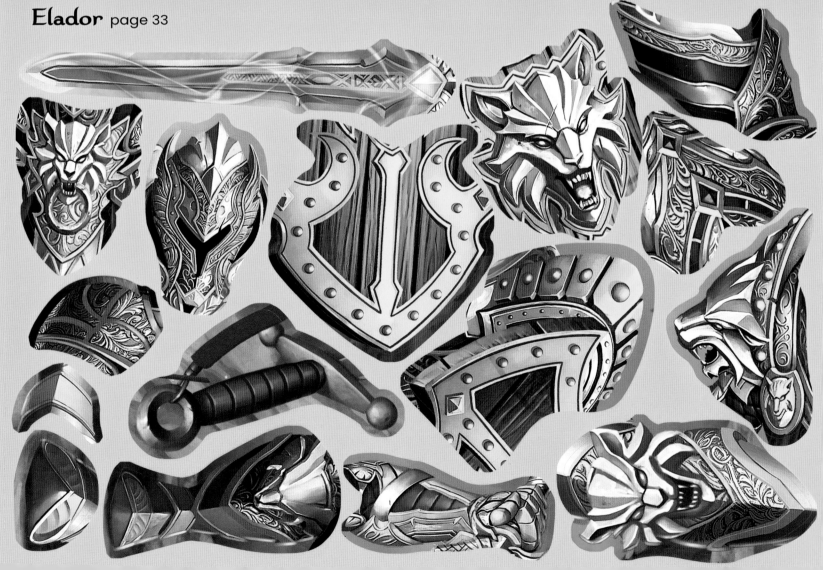

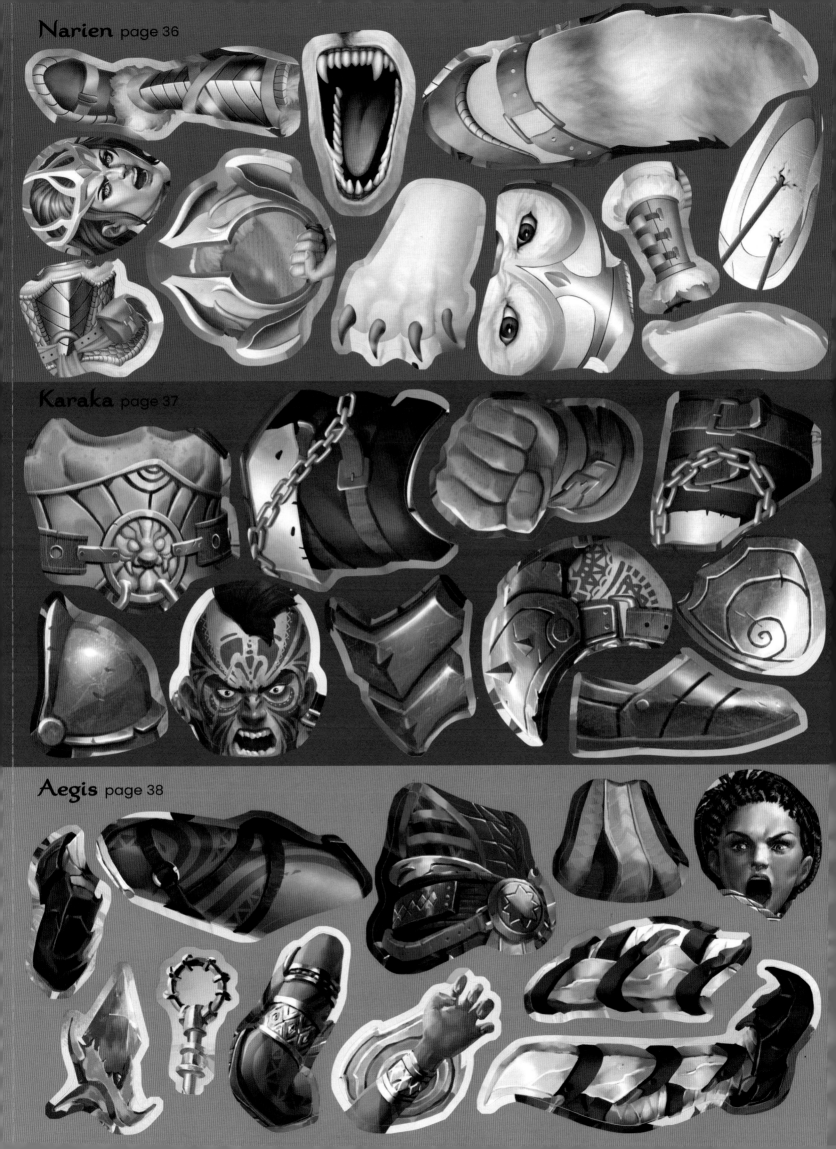

Narien page 36

Karaka page 37

Aegis page 38

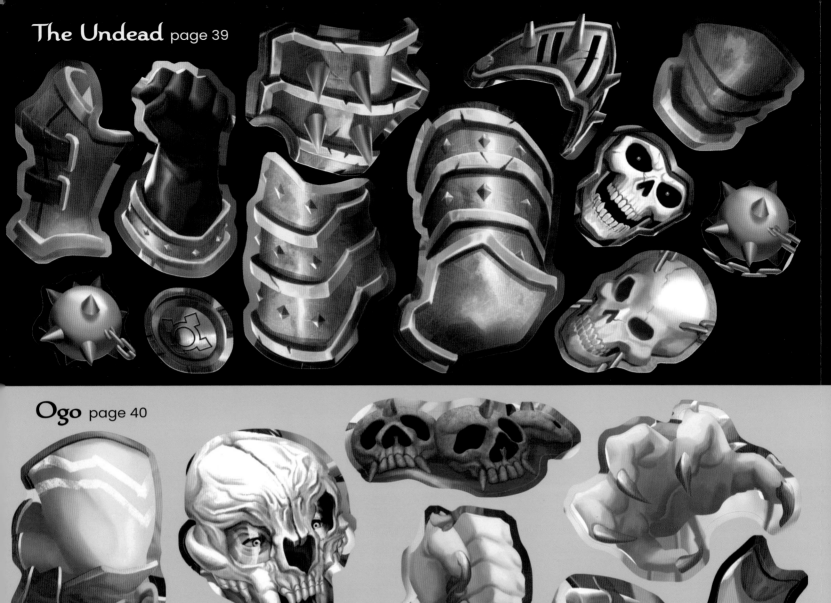

Ogo page 40

Lokus page 41

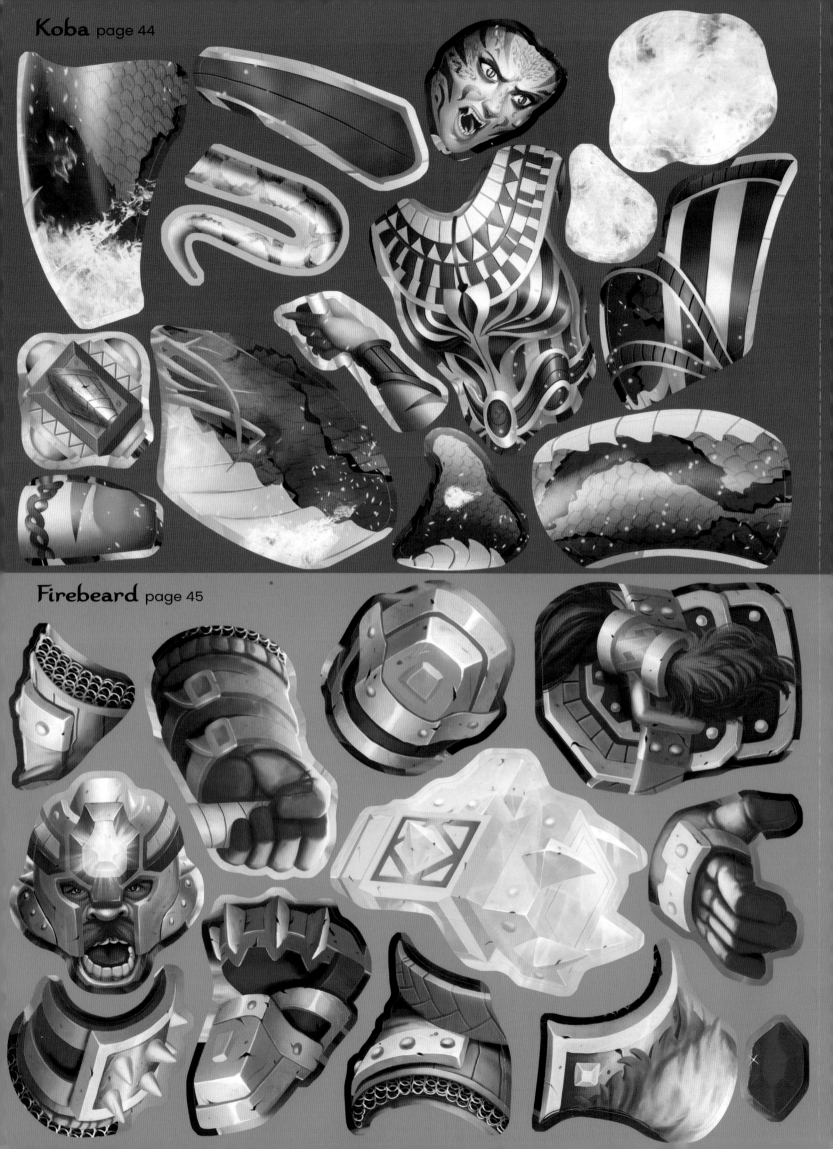